Tales
from The
Deep Dark
Forest

The
KING'S JESTER

Written and Illustrated by Jim Haverland

Writers' Branding
1800-608-6550
www.writersbranding.com
orders@writersbranding.com

Once upon a time,
in the deep, dark forest

there lived a King who was the ruler of the eastern part of the forest.

One day, this kind and benevolent King, decided to add merriment and glee to his Kingdom. He invited everyone to a contest for the highly esteemed position of

The King's Jester!

So he sent out a proclamation declaring August 19th as *The Day of the Jester!*

Within three days, news of the event reached the ears

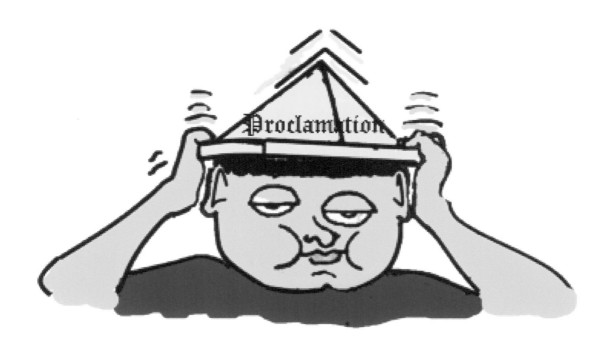

of Napoleon Le Gnome.

Leon, as he preferred to be called,
was unique. For example:

While others made balloon animals,
Leon created balloon worms
and snakes of all sizes!

When he played his kazoo, it was
as if you were at Woodstock!

He was the only man in the Eastern part of
the Forest who could do a *Triple Lindy*!

6

Leon immediately realized this was his chance of a lifetime. If he could win this contest, he would become

The King's Jester!

And so, he began to prepare for
The Day of the Jester!

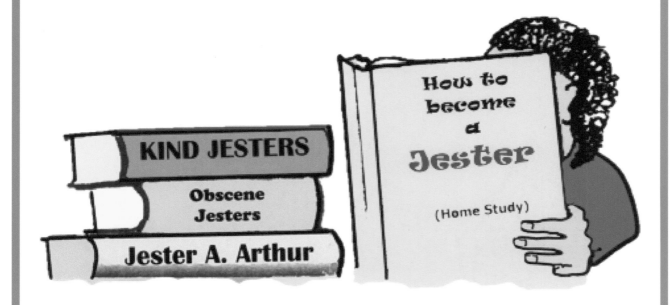

Leon practiced juggling for 3 months,

first one apple,

then two apples,

then eight apples.

Eventually he got to
forty-two apples (and two
and a half worms).

The only thing that stopped him
at forty-two, was a swelling on his
arms which the doctor diagnosed as

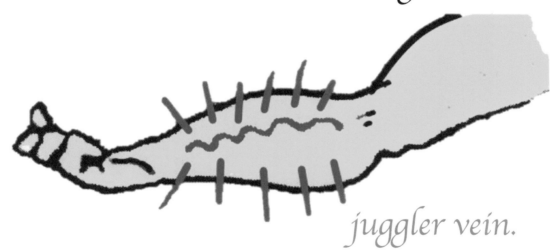

juggler vein.

He learned how to tumble,
how to do flips, and how
to make funny faces.

He even learned a few songs,
and learned how to tell jokes.

Hey! I just flew in from the coast — and boy are my arms tired!!

For months Leon worked hard, and he thought of nothing but his upcoming performance on

The Day of the Jester!

Finally, the day arrived.

1492

August 19

8:00 am:	Set alarm for 8:30 wakeup
10:00am:	Buy more apples
12:00pm:	Lunch on Columbus yacht
2:00pm:	Check for worms in apples
4:30pm	*The Day of the Jester!*

He couldn't wait! He had worked hard, and he loved it. He was confident and he was ready!

Leon stood in front of the King

and his performance was amazing.

He did it all, and he was superb!

Hey, the Police caught the guy who stole my calendar.

He got 12 months!

HA HA HA

NEATO JET!

In fact, not only did he
tickle the King's ribs

but he tickled the King's sauerkraut too!

At this, the King fell apart laughing.

After finally pulling himself together

the King declared,

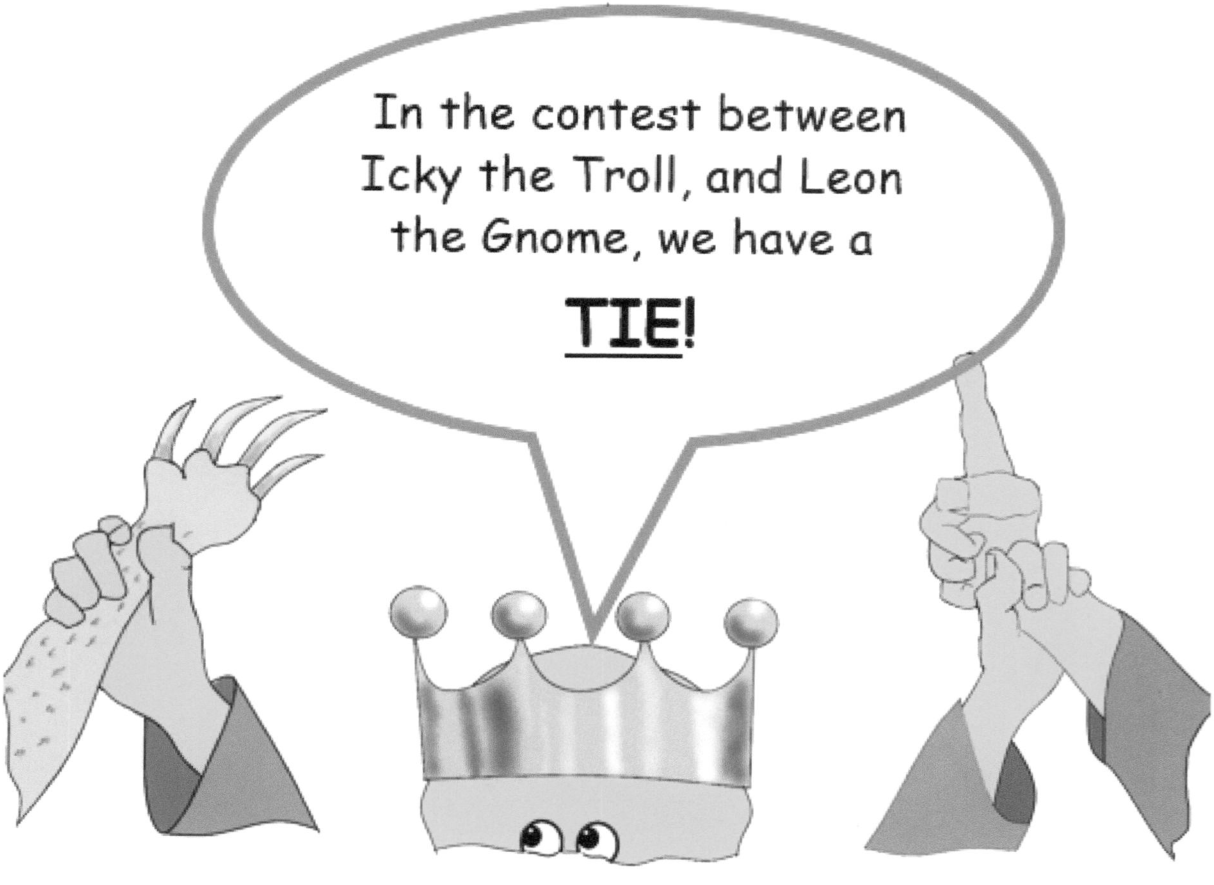

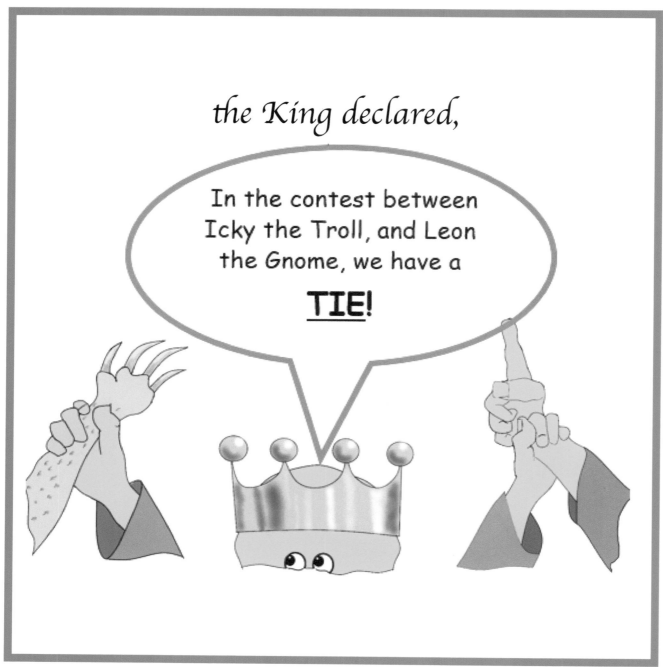

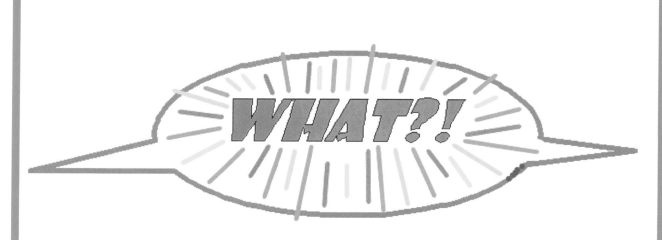

Since the King needed only 1 Jester, he decided that a "Jestoff" was needed, to break the tie.

Icky the Troll and Leon the Gnome would each have 20 minutes to dazzle the King with more of their Jestering skills.

Icky went first.

But Icky just stood there, for 20 minutes, at a loss. He had no more!

It became clear that Icky wasn't really a Jester — he just learned how to do old Jester tricks.

Leon, however, hadn't just learned
old tricks. He created new ones —
his own spectacular repertoire!

Because of all his hard work, his
creativity, and his love of Jestering,
he realized he had become a true

Jester!

Leon stepped back and gave the King another 20 minutes.

He included more new jokes, more new songs, more funny faces, and then he finished it off with — **The Triple Lindy!**

The King was astounded
and declared Leon the new,

King's Jester!

When he was done, he bowed to the King.

The Moral of the Story

Creative ideas and opportunities
are always around us.

Open your mind to see the ones
that excite you the most
and then explore them.

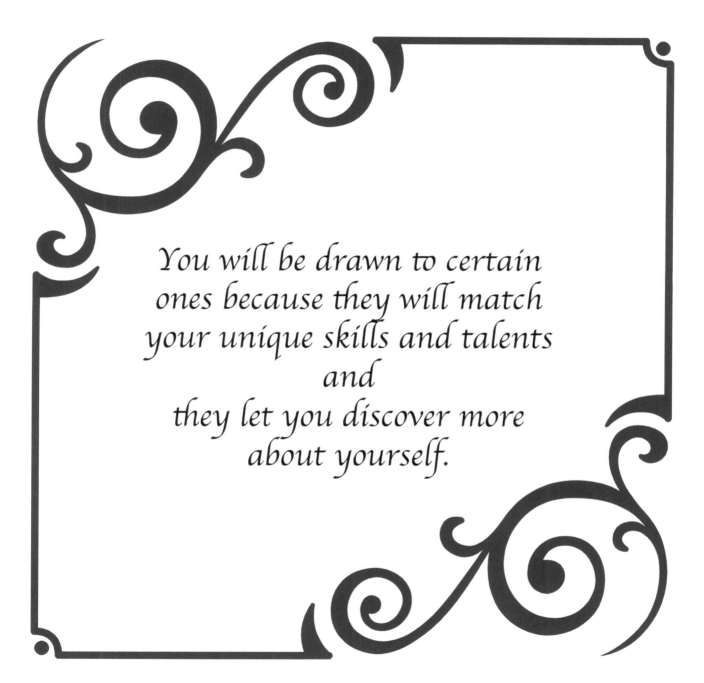

You will be drawn to certain
ones because they will match
your unique skills and talents
and
they let you discover more
about yourself.

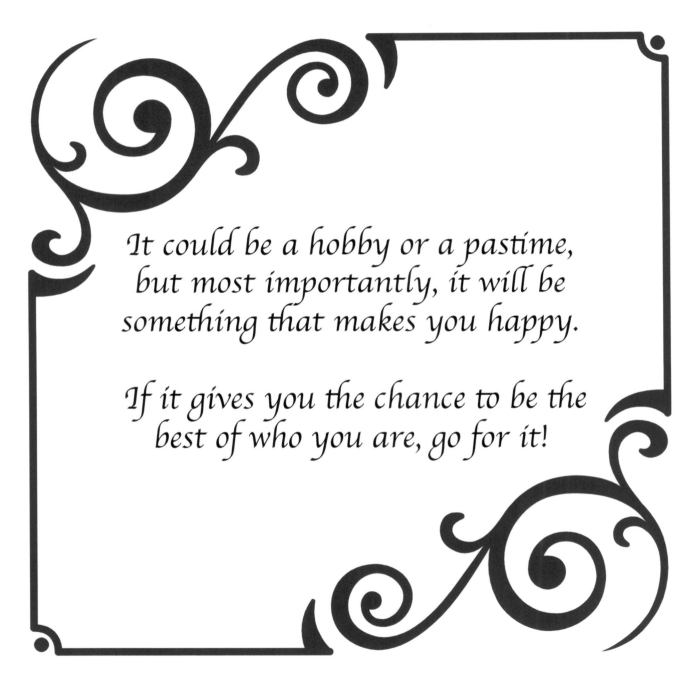

It could be a hobby or a pastime, but most importantly, it will be something that makes you happy.

If it gives you the chance to be the best of who you are, go for it!

Why, you may even have your own

Jesterday

The End.

Grab a copy of these upcoming books of the Tales from the Deep Dark Forest:

The Ugly Man
The Good Robin
The Queen's Stylist
The Weird Witch
The Fiendly Knight
The Fortune Seeker

For more information follow me on Facebook at Facebook.com/AuthorJimH
or
www.BestForestTales.com

Lightning Source UK Ltd.
Milton Keynes UK
UKHW020641101220
374802UK00002B/33